IVOR ENG
A MINER'

JOHN EVANS

Illustrated by Jon Davis

DREF WEN

Ivor England lives in the Rhondda Valley. Ivor is preparing for work. He slips on his waistcoat, knots his scarf around his neck, clips his battery pack to his belt and places his safety helmet on his head. Finally, he picks up his lamp. Now he is ready to start work. Can you guess what his job might be?

Ivor has been working in the pit all his life. He started work as
a coalminer in 1946 when he was fifteen years old. All his friends
and family worked in the Lewis Merthyr Colliery. Ivor remembers
his first day at work. He remembers saying goodbye to his Mam
as she handed him his tommy box and water bottle. He remembers
walking with his father up the hill to the colliery. It was 5.30 in
the morning, and the hooter was sounding to signal the start of
the day shift.

NO SMOKING BEYOND THIS POINT

At the pit head, once he had collected his lamp, Ivor remembers squeezing into the cage with the other miners to take the ride to the pit bottom. Down and down, into the dark, damp mine went the cage. Ivor tried to look brave, but he could feel the butterflies in his stomach. At last the cage reached the pit bottom. The men filed out of the cage, and Ivor blinked in the light of the electric bulbs which lined the roof of the main roadway.

Ivor followed his father and climbed into one of the empty coal
wagons, which would carry them to the coal face where they
would start their work. "It's easy these days!" his father said.
"When I started work twenty-five years ago, we had to walk all
the way to the coal face. There were only pit ponies to pull the
wagons, not electric engines".

All day long, Ivor shovelled the coal on to the conveyor belt. It
was hot and dusty work. All the men chewed tobacco to stop
their mouths becoming dry. At first, Ivor did not like the tobacco,
but he soon got used to it, and it was better than the taste of coal dust.

It took Ivor a long time to get used to working underground. He scraped his elbows and shoulder on the roof of the mine. He had to learn to shovel the coal kneeling down. At the end of his first day, Ivor emerged from the mine at his father's side, tired, aching and covered in coal dust, but proud that he had completed his first day underground. Now they would go to the pit head baths to get cleaned up. "It's easy these days!" Ivor's father said. "When I first started, we had to wash ourselves in a tin bath in the kitchen. Mam-gu had to boil all the water on the kitchen fire."

Although the work was hard, Ivor liked the companionship which working with his friends and neighbours brought. After work he would go to the Miners' Institute, the 'Stiwt' as they called it, to play billiards. On Thursdays he would attend choir practice in the chapel vestry. At weekends, there was the pigeon-cot to clean out and rugby to play, and of course, chapel on Sundays.

Ivor thought that he would work in the mine all his life, like his father, and his grandfather. But things were changing. They had been digging coal from the Lewis Merthyr since 1863. Now it was becoming too difficult and expensive to mine. When the coal arrived at the surface, it was difficult to sell. New fuels were taking over from coal – gas, oil, and nuclear power. Cheaper coal was being bought from other countries. In London, the Prime Minister, Margaret Thatcher, said that it was a waste of money to keep so many mines open. If they could not make money, they must close.

In 1983, the Lewis Merthyr colliery closed. Ivor was out of work and on the dole. He tried to get work in another mine, but there were so many people looking for work that it was impossible. All over the country, mines were closing. The miners said that Mrs Thatcher was trying to destroy their way of life. Didn't she understand that when the mine closed, the community died with it? Ivor saw this happening. The young people left home to look for work elsewhere. Shops went out of business and were boarded up. Even the 'Stiwt' closed down.

In 1984, Arthur Scargill, the Miners' Union leader, announced that all miners throughout Britain would go on strike to protest at what the government was doing. Throughout Wales, Scotland and England the mines fell silent. The striking miners set up picket lines to stop 'blacklegs' working and to prevent the coal leaving the mines.

Sometimes, Ivor would join the picket lines, to feel once again that he was back working with his friends. Although they tried to be peaceful, sometimes tempers were lost and fighting broke out. Lines of people were not enough to stop the coal lorries leaving. The police were called in to charge the picket line with truncheons and riot shields.

13

In the Rhondda, the girlfriends, wives and mothers of the miners supported the strike. They set up a Women's Support Group to collect money and to share out food parcels to the families of the miners.

Some of the women travelled to other parts of Britain to make speeches and to attend meetings to explain why the strike was happening. The women had always thought that it was the men who were doing the important work. Now they felt that they were just as important.

The strike went on for a whole year, and the miners and their families suffered terrible hardship. They did not want to give up the fight for their communities, but it was difficult to find the money to keep going, and the government was so powerful.

On March 5 1985, exactly a year after it started, the strike officially ended. Ivor stood on the road-side and watched the miners march back to work. They carried their banners, and the brass band played at their head. The women marched beside them. They were all proud of what they had tried to do.

Today, no coal is mined in the Rhondda Valleys. There are very few coal mines left in the whole of Wales. But Ivor is working again, back in the Lewis Merthyr colliery, which is now a museum.

Every day he puts on his miner's clothes, picks up his lamp, places his helmet on his head and leads the tourists around the old coal mine. Ivor is an important man. He is one of the few people who still knows what it was really like to be a coal miner.

INDEX